The Perfect You Too

By J. J. Groom

Illustrated by Alyssa Beccue

For Noah, my sunshine on rainy days

Everyone is very different in a special way,

From how we learn and grow
to how we help our friends and play.

You may feel like being different
is something to hide,

But that's not so! You should show
your differences with pride!

Meet four friends:
Āwhina, Caleb, Nina, and Kăi.

They may not be the same,
but they never question why.

They're exactly who they're meant to be,
which doesn't make them blue

Because they are *all*
the perfect them

and *you're* the
perfect you!

Caleb builds great sights
with building bricks the
whole day long

Āwhina tends her garden
as she hums a pretty song.

Nina spends her free time
on her skateboard doing tricks,

Kăi loves to read his books
and look at all the pics.

All of them are different,
and I know that you are too,
but they are all the perfect them
and you're the perfect you!

Draw yourself doing something you love!

Nina loves PE so much, she never has a frown,
Kăi likes English class which makes him jump up and down.

Caleb says that math and science win without a doubt,
Āwhina enjoys art to let her artistic side out.

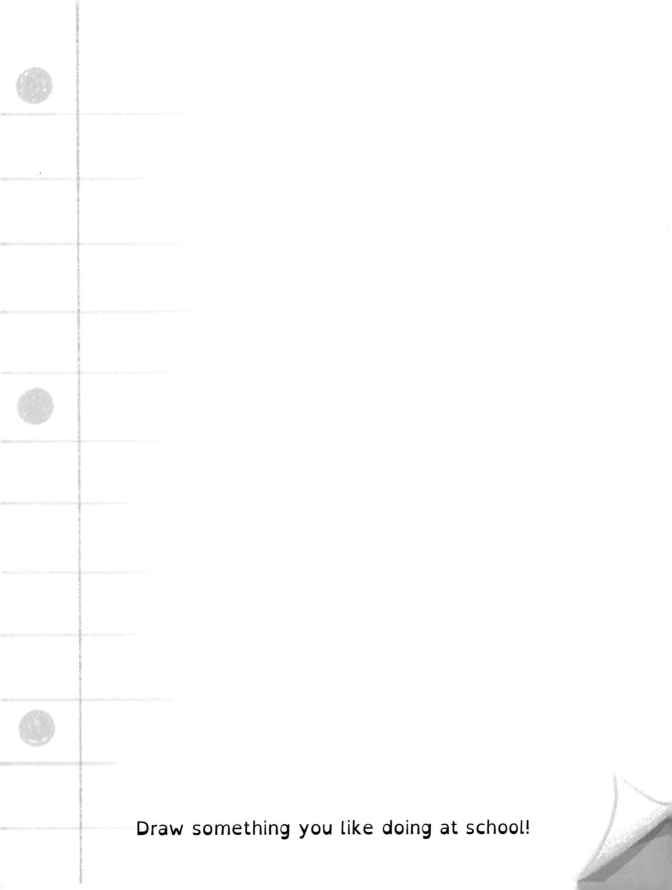

Draw something you like doing at school!

Kăi is shy and quiet 'til he knows you pretty well,
Caleb loves exploring, he has grand stories to tell!

Nina's always first to try out
something new and daring,

Āwhina loves to help her friends,
she is very caring.

All of them are different, and I know that you are too,
but they are *all* the perfect them
and *you're* the perfect you!

Draw something you think represents you!

Āwhina has one sibling that is only one month old,

Caleb's family has two customs, something to behold.

Kăi has two sets
of parents
who both love him
with all their heart,

Nina's parents are
always there,
they are never apart.

All of them are different,
and I know that you are too,

but they are all the perfect them
and you're the perfect you!

Draw what your family looks like!

Caleb enjoys museums,
there's so much to see,

Nina loves concerts
where she can sing and feel carefree.

Āwhina goes to festivals
for dancing, fun, and food,

Kăi knows walking through the park puts him in a good mood.

All of them are different, and I know that you are too,
but they are *all* the perfect them
and *you're* the perfect you!

Draw an activity you enjoy!

Nina wants to take care of the penguins at the zoo,
Caleb dreams of building things from pictures that he drew.

Kăi would like to be a cashier and help everyone,
Āwhina hopes to be a chef whose food can't be outdone.

All of them are different, and I know that you are too,
but they are *all* the perfect them
and *you're* the perfect you!

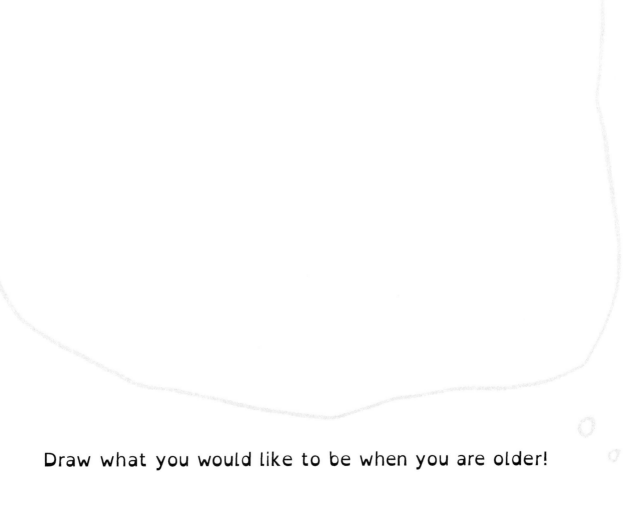

Draw what you would like to be when you are older!

Āwhina has some scars that tell what she's been through,

Kăi's eyes are different colors, one brown and one blue.

Nina has a
prosthetic arm
that she'll
always wear,

Caleb's alopecia
causes him to
lose his hair.

All of them are different,
and I know that you are too,
but they are all the perfect them
and *you're* the perfect you!

Draw something that makes you special!

Now you've learned about these friends
And all their different odds and ends,

You can see what makes you different too.

All these differences make up...

Put a picture of you here!

Made in the USA
Middletown, DE
05 December 2021

54306031R00020